International Pledge for Nurses

In full knowledge of the obligation I am undertaking, I promise to care for the sick with all the skills and understanding I possess without regard for race, creed, color, politics, or social status sparing no effort to conserve life, to alleviate suffering, and to promote health.

I will respect at all times the dignity and religious belief of the patients under my care, holding in confidence all personal information entrusted to me and refraining from any action which might endanger life or health.

I will endeavor to keep my professional knowledge and skills at the highest level and to give loyal support and cooperation to all members of the health team.

I will do my utmost to honor the international code of ethics applied to nursing and to uphold the integrity of the registered professional nurse.

Other books in the **When I Grow Up I Want To Be...**
children's book series by Wigu Publishing:

When I Grow Up I Want To Be...in the U.S. Army!
When I Grow Up I Want To Be...a Teacher!
When I Grow Up I Want To Be...a Firefighter!
When I Grow Up I Want To Be...in the U.S. Navy!
When I Grow Up I Want To Be...a Veterinarian!

Look for these titles in the **When I Grow Up I Want To Be...**
children's book series soon:

When I Grow Up I Want To Be...a Good Person!
When I Grow Up I Want To Be...a World Traveler!
When I Grow Up I Want To Be...a Race Car Driver!
When I Grow Up I Want To Be...a Police Officer!
When I Grow Up I Want To Be... Green!
When I Grow Up I Want To Be...a Rock Star!
When I Grow Up I Want To Be...in the U.S. Air Force!

Cuando Crezca Quiero Ser... coming soon!

Please visit www.whenigrowupbooks.com for more information.
Please like us at www.facebook.com/whenigrowupbooksbywigu.

When I Grow Up I Want To Be...®

a Nurse!

Amber's Accidental Journey

Wigu Publishing | Sun Valley, ID

Library of Congress Control Number: 2014919930
ISBN 978-1-939973-01-6

When I Grow Up I Want To Be… is a registered trademark of Wigu Publishing, LLC. The word Wigu and the Wigu logo are registered trademarks of Wigu Publishing, LLC. The words When I Grow Up… and Cuando Crezca Quiero Ser… are trademarks and/or registered trademarks of Wigu Publishing, LLC.

Wigu Publishing is a collaboration among talented and creative individuals working together to publish informative and fun books for our children. Our titles serve to introduce children to the people in their communities who serve others through their vocations. Wigu's books are unique in that they help our children to visualize the abundant opportunities that exist for them to be successful and to make a difference. Our goal is to inspire the great leaders and thinkers of tomorrow.

First edition, paperback, 2015
10 9 8 7 6 5 4 3 2 1

Quantity sales: Special discounts are available on quantity purchases by corporations, associations, promotional organizations, and others. For details, please contact the publisher at

Wigu Publishing
P.O. Box 1800
Sun Valley, ID 83353
inquiries@wigupublishing.com

Please visit our website at www.whenigrowupbooks.com for more information.

Proudly printed and bound in the United States of America.

This book is proudly dedicated to all nurses, past, present, and future.

Florence Nightingale, known as "The Lady of the Lamp," is a symbol of nursing worldwide.

This is a story about a girl

named Amber. An accident

on the soccer field helps

Amber discover just how

brave she really is!

It was a beautiful day. The sky was blue with a slight cool breeze, and everything seemed just perfect for the first day of soccer practice.

Amber's friends were all running up and down the field.

But not Amber. She was happy just to cheer her friends on from the sidelines.

Amber just had no interest in playing soccer…not one little bit.

Not even when her friends asked her to play, which they always did. Not even when her best friend, Ava, said, "Come on, Amber. We want you on our team. Please?"

Amber always liked being with her friends, especially for birthday parties or sleepovers.

But soccer is hot and sweaty. If you're not running like crazy, you're standing around with tons of parents screaming and playing coach from the sidelines. Some kids even get hurt, she thought. *And practice is sooooooo boring.*

At home later that day, Mom approached Amber and said, "Amber, you know your friends are asking for you to play soccer. If you don't want to do it for yourself, then maybe do it for them."

"They have enough players already. Why do they need me?" asked Amber.

"They want you and are counting on you. What's wrong with that?" said Mom.

Amber thought about it a long time.

"Well, Amber?" asked Mom.

Amber finally agreed. "Fine, I'll play, but I won't like it."

"You never know," said Mom.

I know, thought Amber.

"I'm proud of you," said Mom lovingly. "Just do your best and have fun. Your friends will be so happy."

At Amber's first practice, Coach Harper sat the girls down and said, "We are going to practice smart and work hard on our team soccer skills."

Boring, thought Amber. *Sooooooo boring.*

But as practice went on, something surprised Amber. She started having fun! She started to really look forward to the first game!

This isn't so bad after all, she thought. *It might really be awesome, especially if we win!*

After weeks of practice, game day finally arrived. Both teams sized each other up from across the field.

Amber shuddered.

"They look so big," said Ava.

"They are not just big. They are gigantic! They can't be in our grade," Amber said. "We must be on the wrong field."

They weren't.

Amber gave Dakota a worried glance and asked, "What do you think?"

"I'm thinking what you're thinking. They are huge!" said Dakota.

"Ok, they might have a bit of a size advantage over us, but we've practiced smart and worked hard. We can do this," encouraged Coach Harper.

The referee blew the whistle to start the game. The ball was kicked back and forth and up and down the field and passed from player to player…just like they learned in practice. Then suddenly, someone kicked the ball high in the air.

Players from both teams ran for the ball—and right smack into each other!

There were bumps, clumps, crashes, twists and turns, and feet flying everywhere.

Someone cried, "My nose!"

Something went, "CRACK!"

Amber cried out in pain.

The referee blew his whistle. Everyone stopped and went down on one knee.

Amber's mother ran from the sidelines.

"It hurts," whimpered Amber, cradling her arm.

"My nose is bleeding," cried a girl from the other team.

For a second, Amber almost forgot about her arm. *That's disgusting. I hate bloody noses!*

"You'll be alright," said Mom to both girls. "Anyone else hurt?" All the other girls shook their heads.

"Sofia, gently pinch your nose and hold your head forward. That will help," said the coach from the other team.

"The school nurse, Mrs. Ellis, is still on campus," Coach Harper said. "Let's get these girls over to her office."

This is totally embarrassing! I knew this would happen! Maybe Mrs. Ellis will say it's just a bruise, and I can play again right away, thought Amber, even though she did not really believe it.

What Is a Nurse?

A nurse is someone who takes care of others. It takes a special kind of person to become a nurse.

We often think of nurses working with doctors to help treat sick people, or patients. However, nurses may also do work independently of doctors, like your school nurse does. There are different nurses for different kinds of jobs.

Nurses can perform basic physical exams, give medicine, and perform wound care. Nurses may also conduct research and help educate people about good health habits.

Mrs. Ellis looked over both girls and then asked the girl with the bloody nose to sit down quietly and to keep a tissue against her nose. "I'll get some ice," said Mrs. Ellis. "It should stop bleeding soon."

And it did.

The girl carefully turned toward Amber and asked, "Are you ok? Are you mad at me for knocking into you? My name is Sofia, and I'm really, really sorry. It was an accident, really."

Mrs. Ellis said, "Sofia, hold still, please."

Amber answered, "I'm not mad at you. It was an accident. Are you mad at me? I'm Amber."

"That's a pretty name, and no, you can't be mad if it's an accident. I hope you will be ok soon. Does it still hurt?" asked Sofia.

"Yeah," said Amber. "A lot."

Mrs. Ellis examined Amber's arm carefully. Then she turned to Amber's mom. "I think Amber should go to the hospital emergency room right away. She may have a fracture."

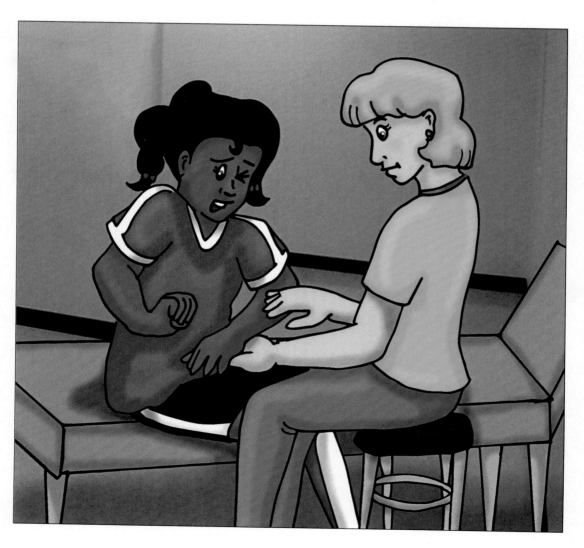

Amber's eyes widened. "What's that?"

"A broken bone," Mom answered, as she turned to Mrs. Ellis. "Do you really think so?"

"I'm afraid it's possible," said Mrs. Ellis.

Amber was afraid, too—afraid of hospitals, needles, and blood! She was afraid the people at the hospital might make her stay overnight and she would be left all alone. She did not want to go at all! She wanted to play soccer with her friends. She did not want to go to any emergency room.

The Emergency Room

An emergency room, or ER, is a section of a hospital for patients who need immediate treatment. The ER is staffed 24 hours a day, seven days a week, and is always ready for a wide range of illnesses and injuries.

The first thing ER workers do is examine the patient to find out how serious the illness or injury is and if anything else is wrong. With that information, they can decide what is best for each patient.

Sometimes, for example, in natural disasters, a large number of injured people arrive at the ER at the same time. ER workers must figure out which patients need help first. This is called a "triage."

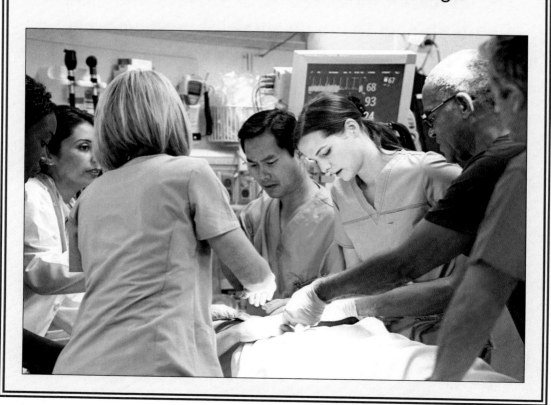

"I am going to put your arm in a temporary splint. The splint will hold your arm in place and protect it until you get to the hospital. Okay, dear?" said Mrs. Ellis.

Mrs. Ellis is always nice. She was nice even that time when I threw up in class, Amber remembered. *That was more disgusting than Sofia's bloody nose. I could never be a school nurse like Mrs. Ellis.*

"I'll call the ER and let them know you're on your way," Mrs. Ellis continued. "You and your mom will go right into the ER, the emergency room. They may X-ray your arm and put it in a cast or splint. Don't worry—they will take very good care of you."

The hospital was a large, white building with a long, circular driveway. Amber had been there before when her brother got his appendix out. A big sign with bold red letters pointed to the emergency room. As Mom drove up, a man in a blue uniform came out to greet them.

"Don't leave me, Mom! Stay right next to me, please," begged Amber.

"I'm not going anywhere but with you, honey," replied Mom.

The man in the blue uniform had a name tag that read, "George Fox, RN."

"It's her arm," said Mom.

"Yes, the school nurse called. We've been expecting you," said George, as he rolled a wheelchair over to Amber.

"It's my arm, not my leg," said Amber, puzzled at the wheelchair.

"My name is George and I'm your ER nurse. It's a hospital rule to put you in a wheelchair to be safe. You look like you've had enough accidents for one day. Besides, you'll like the ride."

Amber sat in the wheelchair. She felt scared, helpless, and embarrassed.

Registered Nurses

A registered nurse, or RN, is a person who has graduated from a college nursing program or received a hospital-based nursing diploma and has passed the national licensing exam.

RNs may care for the sick and injured in places such as hospitals, doctors' offices, private homes, schools, and even at summer camps and vacation spots around the world. RNs are also wellness oriented and are able to assist people in living healthier lives.

Amber was officially admitted to the hospital, and George placed a plastic bracelet on the wrist of her good arm. It had her name and date of birth on it.

Setting down a chart, George examined the splint on Amber's arm. "Looks like your school nurse knew what she was doing. Still hurts a bit though, huh?"

Amber nodded.

Amber just wanted to leave, but instead she asked, "Are you really a nurse? I thought all nurses were girls. I'm sorry if that sounds wrong."

"There are both male and female nurses," George explained. "There always have been, really, and there are all kinds of nurses for all kinds of needs. There are never enough, you know.

History of Nursing

In ancient times, care of the sick and injured was often done by the military or religious groups. Health care was sometimes hard to find.

Florence Nightingale is considered the founder of modern nursing. She was born in 1820 to a wealthy English family who did not think nursing was a proper career for a woman of her status. Against her family's wishes, Florence worked hard to educate herself in the field of medicine, learning as she traveled throughout the world. She became a champion of social reform in England. She worked to improve the health of the poor and raise the standard of living.

"I became a nurse because I like helping people. My father told me long ago that you always feel better when you help someone else," said George.

"That sounds very nice," said Mom. Amber thought so, too.

George asked Mom and Amber a lot of questions about how old Amber was, any other accidents or allergies she had, all about the soccer accident, and if it hurt anywhere else.

It didn't.

"That's a lot of questions," Amber said.

George smiled. "Yep, and the doctor will ask them all over again, just to make sure we didn't miss anything."

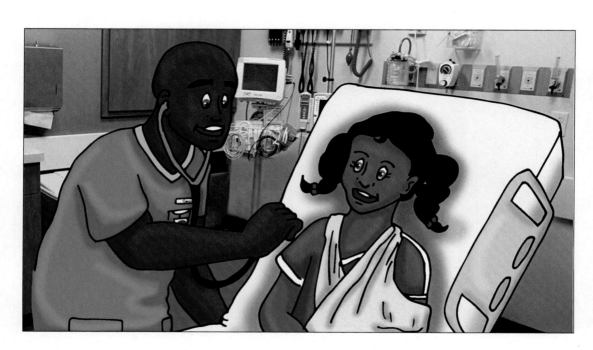

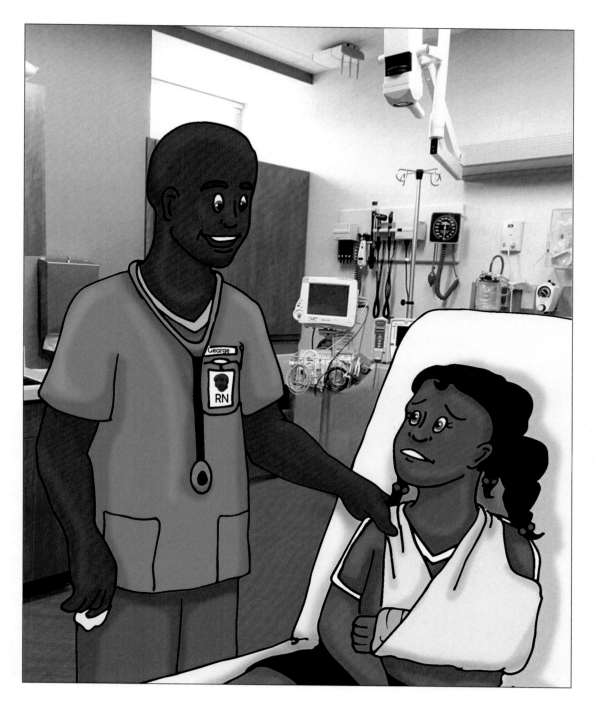

"Am I going to be ok?" asked Amber.

"We'll get you healed up and back to your friends and soccer as soon as possible. Don't worry. You'll be fine," said George.

"I can't wait," said Amber.

"I know," said George. "But first I need to take your vital signs."

"Is that going to hurt?" asked Amber. "Am I getting a shot? Is it going to bleed?"

"This isn't going to hurt at all. I'm just checking how you are overall. I'm making sure you don't have a fever and seeing if there is anything else we need to know," answered George.

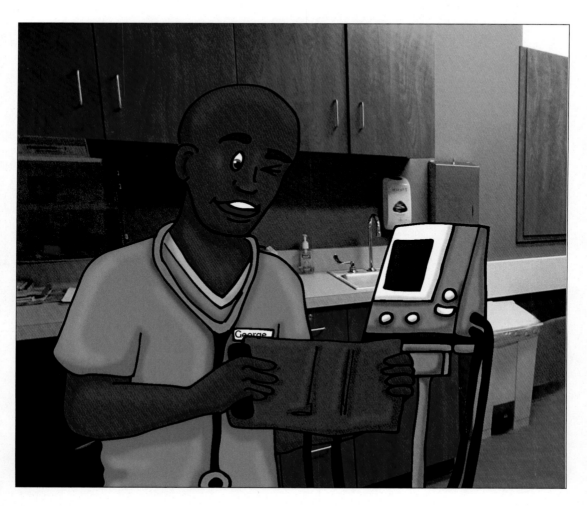

Vitals

When a patient arrives at the ER, the nurse checks his or her vital signs.

Vital signs are measurements of the body's most basic functions:

- Body temperature
- Pulse rate (how fast your heart is beating)
- Respiration rate (rate of breathing)
- Blood pressure

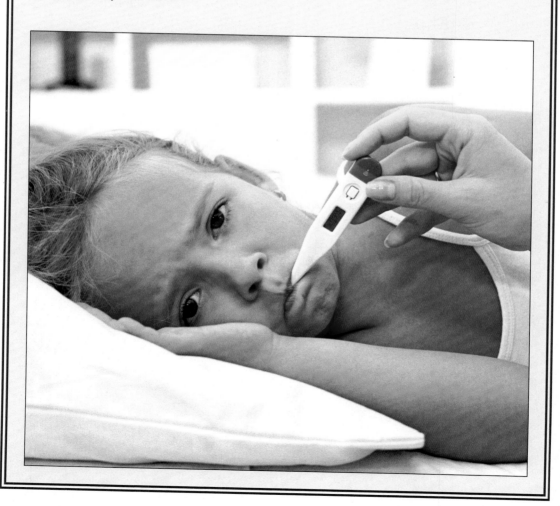

As George was taking Amber's vital signs, a short woman in a white jacket with a stethoscope walked in and asked, "Is this our soccer star?"

"That's me," said Amber, mostly wishing it wasn't.

"Hello, Amber, I'm Dr. Bea." The woman smiled and then asked Amber and her mom the same questions George had.

George looked at Amber and winked.

Dr. Bea looked all over Amber's arm and her neck, legs, and head. "George, let me look at the chart with her vitals."

Dr. Bea studied the chart. "It's most likely a simple fracture. Let's take our soccer star down to radiology to make sure."

"Is it going to hurt?" asked Amber.

"We are just going to have some pictures, called X-rays, taken. Mom, would you please join us?" asked George.

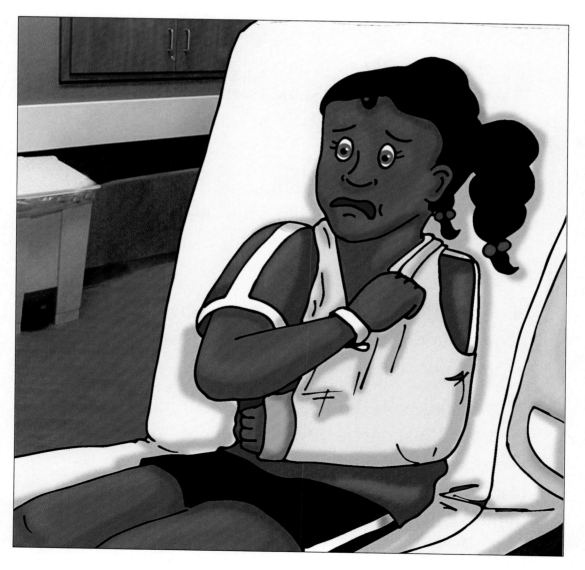

George put Amber back in the wheelchair and took Mom and her down a hall filled with busy doctors and nurses going every which way. George had to navigate the wheelchair to avoid bumping into them.

I've had enough crashes today already, thought Amber.

"There are a lot of doctors and nurses here," said Amber, not wanting to think about what might be next.

"Well, a hospital can be a busy place," said George. "We are all part of the same team, just like your soccer team. But still, there never seems to be enough of us.

"There is a big shortage of nurses throughout the world. I actually worked in China, Africa, and France before I came here. Nurses go all over the world to help people."

"I don't think I want to be a nurse when I grow up. I can't stand looking at blood," said Amber, thinking about Sofia.

"Oh, I think you'd make an excellent nurse," said George. "I used to be afraid of blood, hospitals, doctors, nurses, and needles when I was young. Lots of kids are. Even some adults. You are braver than most."

"Really? Are you just saying that to make me feel better?" asked Amber.

"I am saying it to make you feel better and because it's true," said George, smiling. "When you learn to understand something, it becomes less frightening. You have to be brave and smart, and I think you are both."

George raised his hand and saluted.

Amber saluted back with her good arm.

Overcoming Fears and the "Yuck Factor"

To many people, medical treatment can seem not only frightening but also gross, yucky, or sickening.

Nurses learn to put aside these feelings so they can help others. In nursing school, and in real practice, they come to understand that the things that make the body work do not have to be scary or disgusting at all. Nursing students learn to focus on helping people get better.

At the end of the hallway was a room with a sign that read, "Radiology." The room was filled with big complicated-looking machines and a curly-haired woman with a warm and friendly smile.

"Say hello to Mrs. Sherman," said George.

Amber said hello and then turned to George. "Is this going to hurt?" she asked.

"Only if you fall off the table and break your other arm," joked George. "But we won't let that happen."

"This won't hurt a bit," said Mrs. Sherman. "You'll hear some noise and see some lights from the X-ray machine, but don't let that scare you. It works just like a camera."

Amber still wasn't sure about Mrs. Sherman's machines, but then she thought, *Well, if it's just a camera, I guess it's ok.*

Mrs. Sherman sat Amber in a chair and carefully placed Amber's arm on a metal table next to it. She then put a heavy apron over Amber. "This keeps the X-rays away from the rest of you," she explained.

Mrs. Sherman turned on a light that projected a target on Amber's arm. "This aims the camera, that's all," she said. "Ok, picture time. Hold still, please."

Amber heard a "click" and then saw a flash of light. Then, Mrs. Sherman carefully moved Amber's arm into a different position and there was another "click" and a flash.

"All done, Amber. Great job. That's all there is to it.

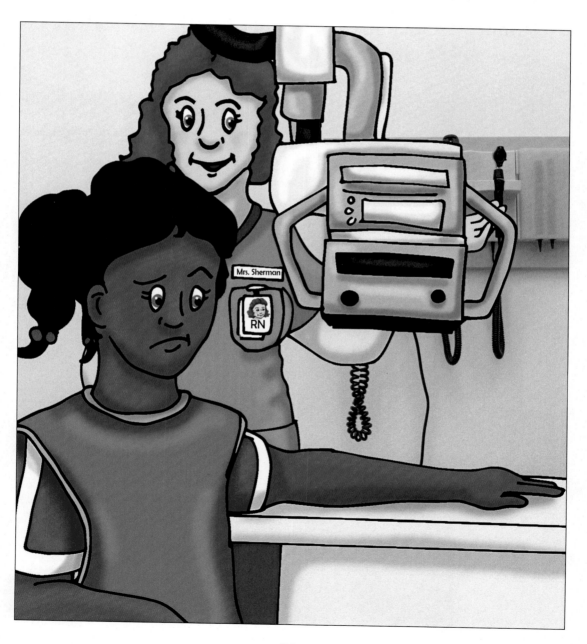

Dr. Bea will review the X-rays when you get back to the ER," said Mrs. Sherman.

"What do X-rays show?" asked Amber.

"They show your bones. We'll see if the bone is broken or not."

Amber decided that was kind of cool. *This isn't as scary as I thought.*

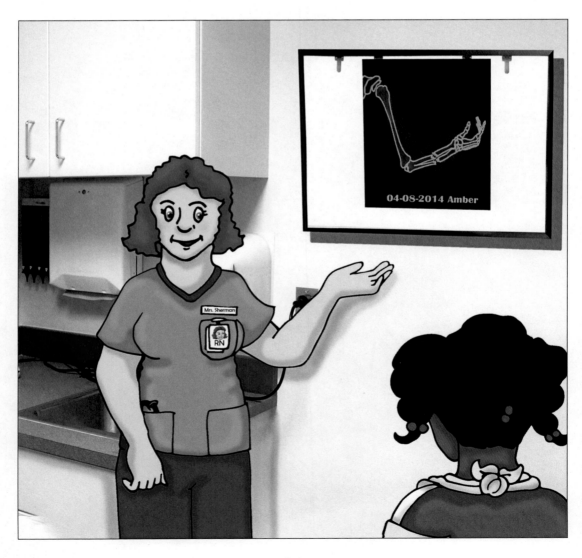

How X-Rays Work

The images made by X-rays are actually shadows.

You see a shadow when light rays from a lamp or the sun are blocked by an object like your body or a tree.

X-rays are like light rays but much stronger. They can pass right through things like skin and muscles, but not bones. Bones block the X-rays and create shadows on the X-ray screen. If there is a break in the bone, that will show up, as well.

X-rays are just one of the many tools used to view what is happening on the inside of your body. Nurses and technicians can specialize in taking X-rays for patients.

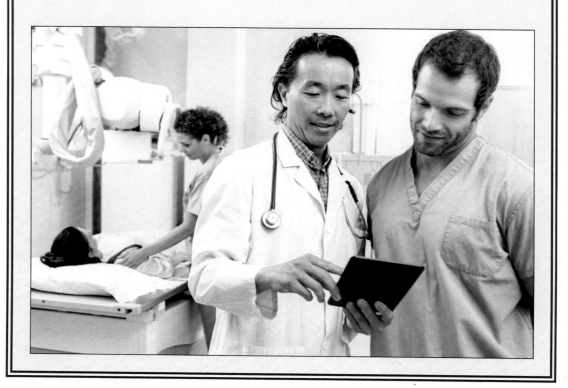

George, Amber, and Mom said good-bye to Mrs. Sherman as George wheeled Amber back down the hall. Mom held Amber's hand.

"I think Dr. Bea needed to check on a patient scheduled for the operating room. She'll be back in a few minutes to look at your X-rays," said George.

"Am I going to the operating room?" Amber asked.

"I doubt it," said George. "The operating rooms are mostly for surgeries."

"Surgeries like taking out an appendix? My brother had his out. Do you do surgeries, too?" asked Amber.

"No. I was trained as an ER nurse, but there are specially trained nurses who work in surgery."

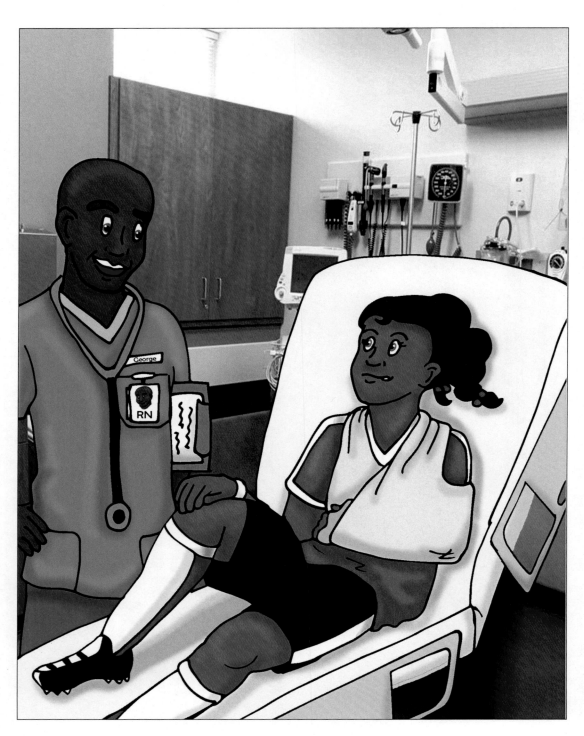

Surgical nurses are just one kind of specialized RN. Their training allows them to assist doctors in performing surgeries.

Circulating nurses move between different surgical assignments, making sure the patient's health information is correct and making sure the patient is ready for treatment.

Scrub nurses set up equipment and handle instruments during surgical procedures.

First assistants help the surgeon with important tasks such as closing a wound or clamping or controlling bleeding.

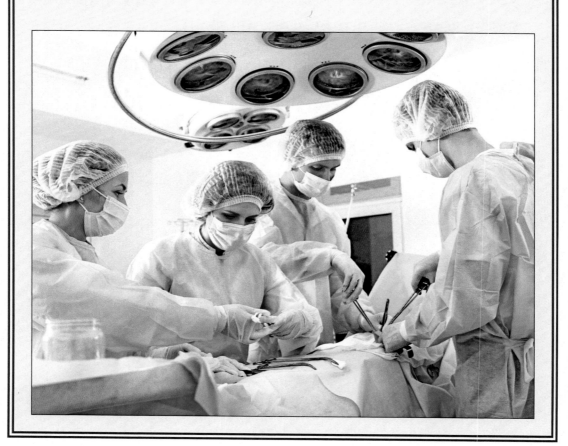

George continued, "After surgery, patients go to a recovery room. Different nurses watch over them there until they get their strength back. Like I said, there are lots of different jobs for nurses. I first learned my job in the U.S. Army."

That explains the salute, thought Amber.

Dr. Bea returned and said, "I just looked at the X-ray images. It's a neat little break, just as I thought. I will show you! If you want, your mom can take a picture of the computer screen with her cell phone, or I can print one out. That way when your friends ask, you can show them what happened when you were going after that ball!"

"Can't I just go home now?" asked Amber.

"As soon as we put on a cast," said Dr. Bea.

"A cast! They won't let me play with a cast!" said Amber. "How long do I have to keep it on?"

"Well, this first cast is temporary until the swelling in your arm goes down. Then you'll get a new one in a few days," Dr. Bea explained. "After that, it may be a few weeks."

"It all depends on how fast you mend," said George. "You'll just have to be patient."

"I am the patient!" said Amber. "Soccer might be totally over by then!"

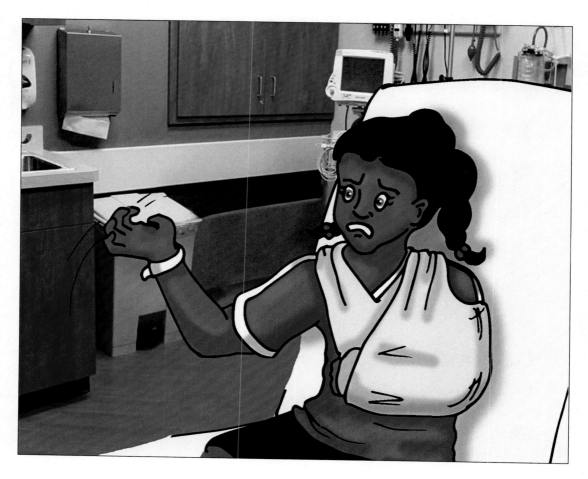

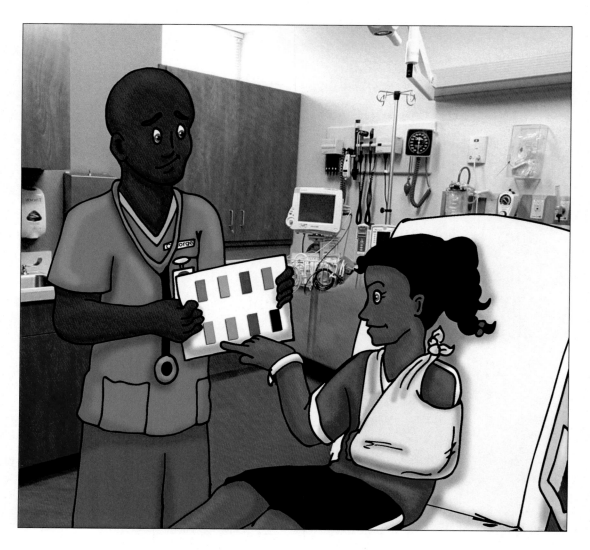

"Your arm needs to heal properly," said Dr. Bea.

"Then you can get back to being a soccer star," said George. "What color cast would you like?"

"Do you have pink?" asked Amber.

"I'm sure we do," said George.

Dr. Bea said, "George, please apply the cast…and make sure it's pink."

George nodded at Dr. Bea and smiled at Amber.

Mom watched while George wrapped Amber's arm in a bright pink cast.

"There!" George announced. "That cast shows everyone how brave you are. You're all set."

Finally, thought Amber.

As Amber left the hospital, she waved good-bye to everyone with her good arm.

"They were very nice," Amber said to her mother.

"Of course they were," said Mom.

On the drive home, Amber looked over her cast. She thought about the school nurse, the hospital nurses, how they all worked together to help her, and how it was not as frightening as she had thought.

"Mom, George said I might be a good nurse when I grow up. What do you think?"

"I think you'd make a wonderful nurse if that's what you want to do," said Mom.

Amber was so glad to finally be home. It was especially nice when her friends called to see how she was.

All the attention made Amber feel special. It was nice when people cared for you, like her friends and the people at the hospital did. Mom always made her feel special.

The next day at school, all of Amber's friends wanted to sign her cast and asked her all sorts of questions about the accident and her visit to the hospital.

In class, her teacher, Mrs. Young, put a gold star sticker on Amber's cast and said, "You sure are brave."

George was right, thought Amber. *I can be brave.*

Amber was especially brave a few days later when she went to her family doctor, Dr. Martin, to have a new hard cast put on her arm. *George was right about that, too,* thought Amber.

The very next Saturday, it was game time again.

"I don't want to go just to watch," Amber pleaded to her mom.

Mom insisted. "You need to go and support your team."

"I'm not sure it's still my team," said Amber, looking at her new pink cast. "I can't even play."

"Of course it's still your team. They'll be happy to see you. And you can cheer them on," said Mom. She was usually right.

Mom helped Amber get her soccer jersey on over her cast, and they drove to the soccer field. When Amber got to the benches, the whole team came over to look at her cast and cheered her return.

Mom was right, thought Amber. *But now I really want to play! But I know I can't...I have to be patient!*

Coach Harper called Amber over and said, "Amber, you are still part of this team. I'd like you to be my assistant coach until you are ready to play again. Deal?"

"Deal!" said Amber, and her teammates roared.

Finally, after what seemed like forever, it was time for Amber to go back to Dr. Martin's office to make sure her arm was ok.

"Can I get my cast off today?" Amber asked. "Can I?"

"I hope so," he said. "Just one quick X-ray and we'll know for sure."

After a "click" and a flash, Amber's doctor gave her the good news. "Looks like you are all healed up and ready to play. I think the nurse can get you out of that cast now."

"Ready to have that cast disappear?" asked the nurse.

"Yes!" *I was ready weeks ago,* thought Amber.

Amber was finally free of the cast, but her arm felt weak and wobbly. The nurse said, "That's because your arm has been in a cast so long."

Way too long, thought Amber. *But maybe the cast is off just in time for the last game of the season!*

"Can I play again?"

"I think that will be fine, but you should still be extra careful," said the nurse.

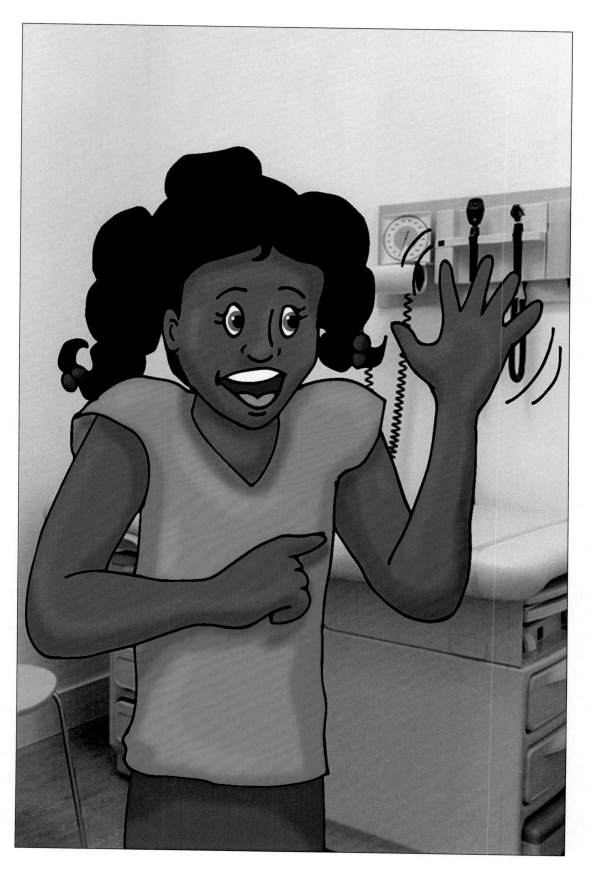

When Amber arrived at the soccer field for the last game of the season, everyone came over to congratulate her. The arm felt fine, but even so, Amber was more than extra careful, especially with the high fives.

To Amber's surprise, someone from the other team was waving at her. It was Sofia. She was playing Sofia's team again! Amber waved back. Sofia yelled across the field, "I'm glad you're back!"

"Me, too!" replied Amber.

The referee tossed a coin. Sofia's team took the left goal and kicked off.

Right at the start, Sofia tripped over the ball and fell right in front of Amber.

Amber reached down and helped Sofia up.

"Thanks!" said Sofia. "I'm good."

"We don't need any more accidents," said Amber, and both girls laughed.

Maybe George was right. When I grow up, I might make a good nurse. I really like helping people, even if they're on the other team! Amber thought.

Sofia dusted herself off and got back into the game. She took the ball and started running toward the goal. Ava took the ball away and passed it to Amber.

Amber was wide open with a straight shot to the goal.

She ran and ran with the wind in her hair. Without stopping, she got ready to kick.

As Amber kicked the ball, she thought, *It doesn't get any better than this!*

GOAL!

Everyone cheered, even Sofia.

That night over dinner, Amber's dad said, "Amber, you've had quite an experience."

"I sure have, Dad. I learned a lot. I learned that I like playing soccer. I learned it feels good to make other people feel good, and I learned that when I grow up, I want to be a nurse!"

"Really?" asked Dad. "How did you discover all that?"

Amber grinned. "By accident!"

Made in the USA
San Bernardino, CA
25 January 2017